for Central Berkshire Girls' Choir

The Old Gumbie Cat

Choral Programme Series

Consultant Editor: Simon Halsey

Memory & other choruses from
CATS

THE OLD GUMBIE CAT · BUSTOPHER JONES
MEMORY · SKIMBLESHANKS

Andrew Lloyd Webber
ARRANGED BY GWYN ARCH

(SSA/Piano)

FABER *ff* MUSIC

CONTENTS

Music Copyright © 1980 and 1981 by The Really Useful Group Limited
Texts by T. S. Eliot Copyright © 1939 by T. S. Eliot;
this edition of the texts © 1980 and 1981 by Set Copyrights Limited
Text of 'Memory' Copyright © 1981 by Trevor Nunn/Set Copyrights Limited
These arrangements Copyright © 1992 by The Really Useful Group Limited
First published in 1992 by Faber Music Ltd
3 Queen Square London WC1N 3AU
Cover design by M & S Tucker
Music processed by Silverfen
Printed in England
All rights reserved

ISBN 0-571-51318-2

To buy Faber Music publications or to find out about the full range of titles available
please contact your local music retailer or Faber Music sales enquiries:
Tel: +44 (0)1279 82 89 82   Fax: +44 (0)1279 82 89 83
Email: sales@fabermusic.com   www.fabermusic.com

Bustopher Jones: the cat about town

Memory

sun - rise, _____ I must think of a new life _____ and I must - n't give

sun - rise, _____ new life, must - n't give

sun - rise, _____ new life, must - n't give

in. _____ When the dawn comes to - night will be a

in. _____ When the dawn comes to - night will be a

in. _____ When the dawn comes to - night will be a

me - mo - ry too, and a new day will be -

me - mo - ry, me - mo - ry too, _____ a new day _____ will be -

me - mo - ry, me - mo - ry too, _____ a new day _____ will be -

* Or a few voices.

Skimbleshanks: the railway cat

* Half-whisper the repeated word *Skimble*.

* Half-whispered.

* Or a few voices.

The Faber Music Choral Programme Series

The acclaimed Choral Programme Series provides a wealth of invaluable concert repertoire for upper-voice choirs, including works by Brahms, Holst, Bridge, Stanford, Warlock, Fauré, Saint-Saëns, Schubert and Schumann, as well as Christmas repertoire, Gospel choruses, arrangements of folk songs and hits from the shows.

Other volumes for upper voices

Carnival! (arranged by Gwyn Arch and Jeremy Browne) ISBN 0-571-51882-6
a brilliant adaptation of Saint-Saëns' Carnival of the Animals

Gaudete! (edited by Jeremy Summerly) ISBN 0-571-51932-6
Medieval songs and carols, including There is no rose and Gaudete Christus est natus

Fly me to the moon and other jazz classics (arranged by Gwyn Arch) ISBN 0-571-52834-1
also including All the things you are, Misty, Moonglow and Caravan

A Gospel Christmas (arranged by Daryl Runswick) ISBN 0-571-51597-5
spirituals for the festive season

Stephen Schwartz *Choruses from 'Godspell' & 'Children of Eden'* ISBN 0-571-51462-6
accessible and practical arrangements by Gwyn Arch

Hamba Lulu (arranged by Mike Brewer) ISBN 0-571-52088-X
five African songs arranged for upper-voice choir with optional percussion

Good News! (arranged by Ken Burton) ISBN 0-571-51918-0
an opportunity to sample the unforgettable wonder of the very best Gospel music

Paul McCartney & Carl Davis *Liverpool Oratorio Selection* ISBN 0-571-51463-4
an entertaining and characterful concert suite arranged for chamber choir

Merry Christmas Everybody! (arranged by Gwyn Arch) ISBN 0-571-51780-3
an irresistible volume featuring some of the very best Christmas pop songs

Benjamin Britten *Three Carols* ISBN 0-571-51860-5
Sweet was the song, A Wealden Trio, and The Oxen

Gabriel Fauré and Camille Saint-Saëns *Six Motets* ISBN 0-571-51483-9
including Ave Maria, Ave verum, and Tantum ergo

Yesterday and other classic pop ballads (arranged by Robert Latham) ISBN 0-571-51823-0
skilful arrangements of some of the best-loved pop ballads of all time

French Motets (edited by Judith Blezzard) ISBN 0-571-51805-2
seven beautiful motets by French composers of the nineteenth century

Johannes Brahms *Eight Romantic Partsongs* ISBN 0-571-51613-0
eight of Brahms's most accessible and rewarding settings for upper voices

Classic English Folksongs (arranged by Robert Latham) ISBN 0-571-51621-1
including Bobby Shaftoe, The Turtle Dove, Scarborough Fair, and Greensleeves

Franz Schubert *Three Partsongs* ISBN 0-571-51309-3
Psalm 23, Gott in der Natur, and Ständchen

Robert Schumann *Eight Partsongs* ISBN 0-571-51470-7
Ländliches Lied, Lied, Erste Begegnung, Liebesgram, Botschaft, Nänie, Triolett, and Spruch

ISBN 0-571-513

FABER MUSIC · 3 QUEEN SQUARE · LONDON
www.fabermusic.com

9 780571 513131